MICHAEL & LAURA FLETCHE

BUILDING

SUCCESSFUL

RELATIONSHIPS

STUDY GUIDE

7 Keys to Winning & Keeping the Hearts of Others

Design by James Richardson.

Contributions by Sarah Boyle, Ron Butler, Elliot Diaz, Chris Floro, Holly Floro, Katharine Floro, Danielle Ledford, Greg Schudel, Ray Warren, & Anna Wiggins.

ISBN-13:
978-0-9976960-1-1
Printed in the United States of America

BREAK THE GROUND

Get to know each other and get your group thinking about the week's topic.

WATCH VIDEO

Each video session provides teaching from Michael and Laura. Play the DVD or stream videos on RightNow Media.[1]

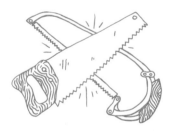

DISCUSS & APPLY

Talk through the content and find ways to apply your insights practically and creatively: from your head, through your heart, to your hands.

JOURNAL

Keep your train of thought going during the group discussion, your devotional times, or throughout the week.

---

[1]Gain free access to RightNow Media at www.rightnow.org/Account/Invite/Manna

CONTENTS

INTRODUCTION

LOVE
Loving others without condition.

FAITH
Believing more for someone than they
believe for themselves.

INTEREST
People are interested in those who are
interested in them.

AVAILABILITY
Being present for someone in their
time of crisis.

RESPECT
Demonstrating a person's value.

TIME
The key to unlocking a heart.

COMMUNICATION
The lifeline of any relationship.

Proverbs 4:23 tells us, "Keep your heart with all diligence, for out of it spring the issues of life." (NKJV) In other words, all of life grows out of our hearts, and that includes all of our relationships: marriages, families, friends, coworkers, you name it. All of those relationships begin when one person's heart is won by someone else, sometimes without either of them knowing it. And we keep someone's heart by doing the same things we did to win it. The trouble is, we often don't realize what things we did—and the more we open our hearts to others, the greater our risk of being hurt. The good news is that we don't have to continue taking a hit-or-miss approach to the relationships that can impact us so deeply. There are seven powerful keys that win and keep hearts when we apply them: Love, Faith, Interest, Availability, Respect, Time, and Communication.

Over the next seven weeks, we're going to study each of these keys in detail, learning how each one works to open hearts and how we can creatively use them to cultivate strong, lasting relationships in all walks of life. Whether you want to see a good relationship become great, repair a relationship that may be faltering, or begin a new one, it's the purpose of this study to equip you with the relational tools you need.

As we get started, bear in mind that this study guide and the accompanying videos are intended to supplement the Building Successful Relationships sermon series and/or the book. We invite you to use either (or both!) as your group gets under way.

The Session Blueprints on page 4 will give you a bird's-eye view of how each group session should flow, but remember: this workbook is a guide, not a straightjacket. If your group responds to the lesson in an unexpected way—if you think of a better question than the ones in the workbook—if you never get past the first question or two each session, don't worry! As we said, relationships are the most important part of our lives, and your group is first and foremost about relationship. Take the opportunity to start applying the principles we'll study each week. If this happens to be your first time hosting (or co-hosting) a group, we invite you to take a look at page 84 for some pointers to help you hit the ground running.

Remember this—whoever has your heart has your life. Perhaps your heart has been hurt over the years by relationships with family members, lovers, friends, or coworkers whose hearts you lost. Perhaps you're searching for ways to strengthen and deepen relationships you have. Perhaps you simply want a friend. Wherever you may be, the principles we'll explore in this study can change your life for the better. It's going to be a great ride, and we're so glad you're joining us for it! Let's get building.

MICHAEL & LAURA

For God so loved the world that he gave his one and only Son, that whoever believes in him shall not perish but have eternal life.

John 3:16

LOVE

SESSION 1

LOVING OTHERS WITHOUT CONDITION

BREAK THE GROUND

What is love, really? Some people will tell you it's just an emotion. Some think it's infatuation—as in, "I've loved him since the first day of class!" Others confuse it with lust. Sometimes we mistake needing someone for loving someone, the way parents sometimes "love" a child as long as that child performs well. But these skewed forms of love are all focused on what we receive from someone else. The heart of true love is *giving*.

What else would you say defines true love?

WATCH VIDEO

- Proverbs 4:23— "Guard your_____ with all diligence, for out of it flow the_____." (NKJV)

- Theologians say the heart is the center of the _____.

- All of _____ flows out of the heart.

- Whoever has the _____ has the _____.

- How you_____ a heart is how you _____ a heart.

- John 3:16— "For God so loved the world that he _____ his only begotten Son…"

- _____ is the opposite of love.

- The love God has for us is without _____.

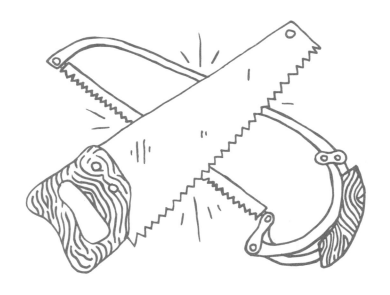

DISCUSS & APPLY

1. In the video, Michael and Laura emphasized Proverbs 4:23. Can you share an example of how life flows from the heart?

2. According to John 3:16, what is God's definition of love? How can we tell the difference between true and false forms of love (emotion, infatuation, lust, or need-love)?

3. Why are people afraid to give love without expecting anything in return?

4. What does unconditional love look like in marriage? Between parents and children?

5. First Peter 4:8 says, *"Above all, love each other deeply, because love covers over a multitude of sins."* What does this verse tell us about unconditional love? Is covering sin the same as ignoring it?

6. Correction, when properly administered, is loving. How do correction and love work together?

7. Read 1 Corinthians 13:4-8— *"⁴ Love is patient, love is kind. It does not envy, it does not boast, it is not proud. ⁵ It is not rude, it is not self-seeking, it is not easily angered, it keeps no record of wrongs. ⁶ Love does not delight in evil but rejoices with the truth. ⁷ It always protects, always trusts, always hopes, always perseveres. ⁸ Love never fails. But where there are prophecies, they will cease; where there are tongues, they will be stilled; where there is knowledge, it will pass away."* How can the Church show this kind of love to those who don't believe?

8. As a group, one of the best ways to share the love that Christ freely gave us is to freely give it to others. Begin to plan an outreach that the group can conduct within the next seven weeks to show your community that Christ's love is free, no strings attached.

Outreach Ideas

- Conduct random acts of kindness by paying for someone's meal, coffee, gas, laundry, etc.

- Provide a meal for a family outside your small group.

- Provide practical help for someone in need: yard work, fixing something inside a home, an oil change, clothing, etc.

- Prayer walk a neighborhood.

- Volunteer at a local food bank, soup kitchen, or other charitable organization.

- Participate in an outreach with your local church.

- Contact The Fayetteville Dream Center and assist with any projects they are working on.

- Adopt a family for Christmas.

- Provide a meal to first responders in your area.

- Serve at a nursing home.

- Conduct a water bottle giveaway.

- Serve free coffee and snacks at the emergency room.

- Throw a block party for your neighborhood.

- Other: _____

JOURNAL

What personal barriers discourage you from giving unconditional love to others? How can you work towards overcoming those barriers?

Most of us have at least one relationship that we feel needs some improvement. Choose a relationship in your life that you think fits that description (spouse, child, friend, etc). Brainstorm some tangible, practical ways that you can show unconditional love to that person this week.

But encourage one another daily, as long as it is called Today, so that none of you may be hardened by sin's deceitfulness.

Hebrews 3:13

FAITH

SESSION 2

BELIEVING MORE FOR SOMEONE
THAN THEY DO FOR THEMSELVES

BREAK THE GROUND

What does it mean to have faith for a person? It means that we believe in them more than they believe in themselves. Hebrews 3:13 tells us to "encourage one another daily." The word "encourage" literally means "to give courage." When we see more for a person than they can see for themselves, we give them the courage to move on, face obstacles that seemed impossible, and find new ways of thinking. We build their confidence—and as we do, we find a curious thing happening. That person starts to depend on us. That person starts to trust us. That person wants to be around us. When you have faith for someone, you win their heart.

What's the most inspiring film you ever watched?

What part did faith play in the story?

WATCH VIDEO

- Proverbs 4:23—"Guard your heart with _____, for out of it flow the issues of life." (NKJV)

- All of life comes from the _____.

- Faith is _____ for someone than they believe for themselves.

- The way to keep someone from sin and move them forward in their walk with God is _____ (Hebrews 3:13).

- Faith is seeing another person through _____.

- God sees us as _____, not as we are.

- When you see someone through God's eyes, you give them _____.

- The greatest agent of world-change is _____, not _____.

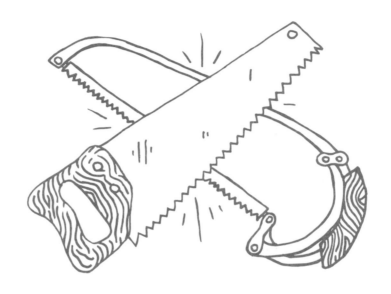

DISCUSS & APPLY

1. Can you think of a time when someone expressed faith for you and changed your view of yourself, your future, or the obstacle you were facing?

2. Why is someone's faith in you such a powerful motivator?

3. In the context of Proverbs 4:23, what happens when someone receives discouragement from their loved ones, instead of encouragement?

4. Discuss the relationship between faith and unconditional love. Can you have one without the other?

5. Proverbs 27:6 and Hebrews 3:13 imply that we have a responsibility to build one another up through correction when necessary. How can we speak correcting truth to someone without discouraging them?

6. How might God use you to encourage your spouse/friend/family members/coworkers in their faith? In their dreams? In their work? In their struggles or challenges?

7. Sometimes we see a future for others based on what we ourselves want. How does having faith for our loved ones differ from having an agenda for them?

8. Read Acts 9:10-17. Why did Ananias have faith for Paul? How can we as the Church imitate this kind of faith for one another?

JOURNAL

Think of three people who are close to your heart right now. What adjectives do you think God would use to describe them?

How can you show these people every day how God views them? What is it that you like about their character or habits (look specifically for things that do not personally benefit you)?

Who is the most encouraging person in your life right now? Take a moment this week to thank that person for their faith for you.

Do nothing out of selfish ambition or vain conceit, but in humility consider others better than yourselves. Each of you should look not only to your own interests, but also to the interests of others.

Philippians 2:3-4

INTEREST

SESSION 3

VALUING WHAT OTHERS VALUE

BREAK THE GROUND

When you express interest in something that's important to your spouse or child or friend, you are also expressing interest in them. You've given them freedom to share what is close to their heart. There's no better example of this principle than Jesus. In Philippians 2:6-8 Paul tells us that Jesus "did not consider equality with God something to be grasped, but made himself nothing, taking the very nature of a servant..." He completely set aside his own interests to care for the interests of others. How many hearts have been won by Jesus over the last two thousand years, do you think? The same principle will work in your life.

When was the last time you discovered you had an interest or passion in common with someone?

What effect did that discovery have on your relationship?

WATCH VIDEO

- Proverbs 4:23—"Guard your heart with all diligence, for out of it _____." (NKJV)

- Whatever you did to _____ a heart is what you do to _____.

- Interest is _____ what is important to others.

- Philippians 2:3—"Do nothing out of selfish ambition or vain conceit, but in humility _____."

- When you show interest in what interests somebody else, they take your interest as _____.

- Everyone is glad to find _____.

- Everyone wants to be valued, appreciated, and _____.

- Parents: This principle can _____ your kids' hearts to you.

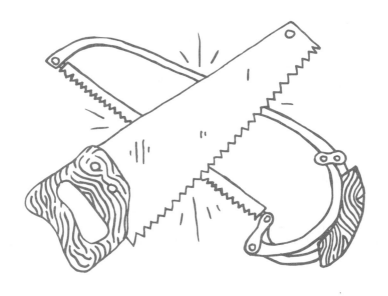

DISCUSS & APPLY

1. What are some of the results that come from investing one's time in what interests someone else?

2. Bearing in mind Proverbs 4:23, what happens in our hearts when someone gives their time to something we're interested in, particularly when they do not share the same interest?

3. How does sharing interests affect trust between two people?

4. How can we show interest in something that does not naturally interest us?

5. How can we stay in sync with our children's changing interests and build them up when we spend time doing things they like to do?

6. How does your ability to take an interest in someone else's passions or hobbies reflect your character?

7. How might you let go of self to genuinely give value to the interests of your spouse?

8. In what ways did Jesus model Philippians 2:3-4? How can we imitate Him as individuals? How can the Church imitate Jesus' example in its interactions with the world?

three

JOURNAL

In your top three relationships, what are the main interests of those people? List at least three per person.

How can you demonstrate interest in those things? Think specifically and practically.

A new command I give you: Love one another. As I have loved you, so you must love one another.

John 13:34

Carry each other's burdens, and in this way you will fulfill the law of Christ.

Galatians 6:2

AVAILABILITY

SESSION 4

MAKING ROOM FOR OTHERS IN CRISIS

BREAK THE GROUND

W e tend to throw the word "availability" around lightly. People will say, "He knows I'm available; he can call me any time." Availability means more than just being a crisis hotline number someone can call if needed. When you make yourself available to someone, you make a commitment to be there in the crisis and to stay through the end. Deep and lasting bonds grow between people who walk through the valley together. The heart of someone in crisis is begging to be heard and understood. Be the person who listens.

How would you define a crisis?

four

WATCH VIDEO

- Proverbs 4:23—"_____, for out of it flow the issues of life." (NKJV)

- Whoever has the _____ has the person.

- Availability is making room for others in _____ and in _____.

- Galatians 6:2—"Carry one another's _____, and in this way you will fulfill the law of Christ."

- Crisis is a huge _____.

- You don't have to have all the _____.

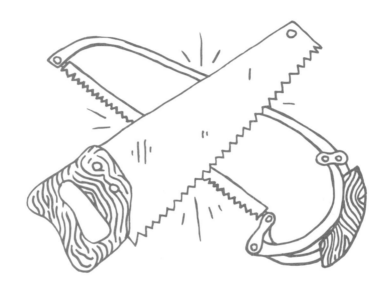

DISCUSS & APPLY

1. Have you ever seized (or missed) an opportunity to be available to someone going through a crisis? What was the effect on your relationship?

2. Galatians 6:2 tells us to "carry one another's burdens." What do you think this means practically?

3. Is availability just a question of time? In what other ways should we be available to our loved ones?

4. Michael said that a crisis should be defined by the person going through it. If you have a close relationship with someone, does this give you a voice in defining what is or isn't a crisis for them? Why, or why not?

5. Read Luke 5:17-20. Jesus was willing to be interrupted in times of crisis, because He never forgot that His primary purpose was to restore our relationships with Him. How can we maintain a similar attitude?

6. Read Mark 6:31-34. What do you think made it possible for Jesus to be available to the crowd even when he was physically exhausted?

7. Proverbs 4:23 warns, "Guard your heart..." (NKJV) How can we keep our hearts from being hardened by those who might abuse our availability?

8. If relationships are built by winning hearts, how should the church respond to crises in our community?

four

J O U R N A L

Who has been there for you when the chips were down? Describe your feelings toward those people. Why do you feel that way?

What are the barriers to your availability? Are they practical (such as a full schedule)? Are they emotional?

What steps can you take to guard your heart while still making it open to others?

Give everyone what you owe him…if respect, then respect; if honor, then honor.

Romans 13:7

RESPECT

SESSION 5

ESTABLISHING A PERSON'S WORTH

BREAK THE GROUND

M ost of us think of respect as something that someone has to earn from us. We see ourselves on a ladder—we give respect to those we think are above us, and we sometimes fear that if we give respect to those below us, we'll make ourselves look weak or insignificant. The truth is actually the reverse. Respect should always be founded on merit—but everybody has some expertise that you don't. Treat them like they're on a higher rung of the ladder, and you'll put yourself in a position to win—or keep—their hearts.

According to our culture, what makes someone worthy of respect?

five

53

WATCH VIDEO

- Proverbs _____ —"Guard your heart _____ , for out of it flow_____ ." (NKJV)

- Whoever has the heart _____ .

- Respect is _____ a person's worth.

- Romans 13:7—"Give everyone what you owe him...if _____ , then respect; if _____ , then honor."

- Every person deserves some measure of respect because they were created _____ .

- Every person desires to be _____ , accepted, and honored.

- Respect where it's not _____ is powerful.

- Respect is a _____ ; we can get good at it.

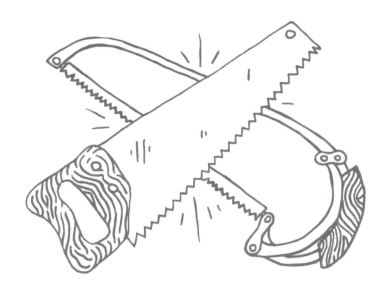

DISCUSS & APPLY

1. What makes you feel respected?

2. Why do we tend to evaluate people's worth according to their station?

3. If respect means establishing a person's worth, how did God demonstrate respect for us as human beings?

4. Read Proverbs 4:23. What does your respect for others communicate about God's heart towards them?

5. How does respect balance with love in a marriage?

6. What role do you think pride and humility play when we respect those we lead?

7. How do you respect someone when you think their behavior doesn't merit respect?

8. Do you think most non-believers would agree that the Church respects them? What steps might we take as the Church to communicate respect to those outside?

five

JOURNAL

Our ability to give respect is often tied to how much we respect ourselves. What conclusions might you draw about yourself as you consider the following:

- Is your opinion of others influenced by their economic, educational, or social status?
- Do you find it difficult to let someone else be the expert?
- How do you respond when someone surpasses you in an area of your expertise?
- Does your respect for yourself change depending on what others think of you?

What changes in you when you respect another person's value, rather than focusing on their faults?

There is a time for everything, and a season for every activity under heaven…

Ecclesiastes 3:1

See then that you walk circumspectly, not as fools but as wise, redeeming the time, because the days are evil.

Ephesians 5:15-16 (NKJV)

TIME

SESSION 6

THE KEY TO UNLOCKING A HEART

BREAK THE GROUND

Our life is literally time. Every one of us gets sixty seconds a minute, twenty-four hours a day, three hundred and sixty-five days every year; and the way we use that time is the measure of what we really value. It doesn't take very long to tell your son, "I love you"—but when you spend three hours of your Saturday cheering on his Little League team, you show that the words have meaning. If you want to make someone a priority in your heart—and thus win a place in *their* heart—you must make them a priority in your schedule.

Even though we all get twenty-four hours a day,
why do we so often feel that we don't have enough time?

six

WATCH VIDEO

- _____ 4:23 — "_____ your _____ with all _____ , for out of it _____ the _____ of _____." (NKJV)

- Whoever _____ has the person.

- Time is the key to _____ the heart.

- Ephesians 5:15-16 — "See then that you walk circumspectly, not as fools but as wise, _____ the time, because the days are _____." (NKJV)

- Time is the _____ of relationships.

- You can use time as a _____.

- If you spend time with someone, you will gain _____, negatively or positively.

- If you _____ spending time with someone, the relationship will wane.

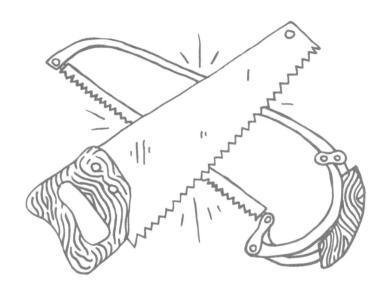

DISCUSS & APPLY

1. Do you have any relationships that wouldn't have existed if you had not spent a lot of time with that person? Share your story.

2. Why does spending time with someone put us in a position to capture their hearts, or them in a position to capture ours?

3. If time is the currency of relationships, how do you intentionally or unintentionally communicate other people's value with your time?

4. If, as Proverbs 4:23 tells us, whoever has our heart has our life, what criteria should we use when prioritizing the way we spend our time?

5. If love is spelled "T-I-M-E", and not all time spent together is equal, what kinds of activities yield the best return?

6. What benefits do you reap from spending time alone with your spouse/children/etc.?

7. Under what circumstances would it be a poor decision to invest too much time with someone? Why is an "emotional affair" just as detrimental as a physical affair?

8. Ephesians 5:15-16 advises us to "walk circumspectly...redeeming the time, because the days are evil." (NKJV) As members of the body of Christ, how can we advance the Kingdom of God by investing our time in the world around us?

JOURNAL

The real measure of what we value is how we live our lives in relation to time. This week, set aside a time to prayerfully evaluate your schedule and ask for guidance on how you can use your time with increasing wisdom. Use these questions to help you reflect:

Who is really important to you? Rank them. Does your boss come before your spouse, or your clients before your kids?

1.
2.
3.
4.

How can you make the most of the parts of your schedule that you don't control—chores, commutes, the kids' soccer games, etc.?

1.
2.
3.
4.

What is most important to your loved ones? Time invested in these activities will yield the highest returns.

1.
2.
3.
4.

Are there any places in your life where time could become a trap to you—a coworker whom you're attracted to, an addictive game on your phone, etc.?

1.
2.
3.
4.

Let no unwholesome word proceed from your mouth, but only such a word as is good for edification according to the need of the moment, that it may give grace to those who hear.

Ephesians 4:29 (NASB)

COMMUNICATION

SESSION 7

THE LIFELINE TO EVERY RELATIONSHIP

BREAK THE GROUND

Each one of your relationships depends on communication. Love, availability, faith, respect, all the other keys we've discussed will fail if you don't communicate them to the other person. Solomon tells us in Proverbs 18:21 that "Death and life are in the power of the tongue." (NKJV) Your words to your loved ones can destroy and wound—but you can also impart affection, give strength, open someone's mind to new possibilities, and comfort a wounded heart. Communication of this nature wins the hearts of those around you and nurtures their life.

As a kid, did you ever say, "Sticks and stones can break my bones but words will never hurt me"?

Was it true then? Is it true now?

seven

WATCH VIDEO

- Communication is the _____ to every relationship.

- Ephesians 4:29—"Let no unwholesome word proceed from your mouth, but only such a word as is good for _____ according to the need of the moment, that it may give _____ to those who hear." (NASB)

- Edification means _____.

- Resolution to conflict is always found in _____.

- Communication is the most _____ of the seven keys.

- Almost every time a relationship wanes, there has been a _____ in communication.

- Get rid of _____ words and start speaking _____ words.

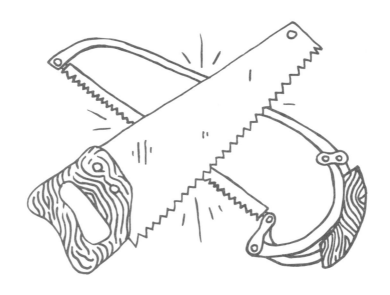

DISCUSS & APPLY

1. Read Proverbs 15:4. In what ways can our words be "a tree of life"?

2. Proverbs 15:4 also says that the deceitful tongue crushes the spirit. Have you seen or experienced this?

3. Read Luke 6:45. How does the way that we communicate reveal the state of our hearts?

4. Why do Michael and Laura say that "silence is lethal" in relationships?

5. Do our words impact only the person to whom we speak? Who else might be affected, either positively or negatively?

6. In what ways do we teach children the importance of words? How can you become more intentional about modeling life-giving communication?

7. Proverbs 4:23 reminds us that all of life flows from the heart. How can words bring life (or death) to a church body?

8. Second Corinthians 5:20 says we are Christ's ambassadors. How do the words we speak portray Jesus to the world around us?

JOURNAL

Read the list of destructive forms of communication on the following page. Do you ever employ any of these in your relationships?

Read the list of constructive forms of communication. Which ones come most naturally to you? Which might you need to work on?

If God only used the words you speak to others to judge you—what conclusion would He come to?

DESTRUCTIVE WORDS

angry words	lying (exaggeration)
hasty words	flattery
rash words	gossip
harsh words	slander
condemning words	complaining
unkind words	cursing
bitter words	quarreling
mocking words	scoffing
foolish words	comparison
critical words	backbiting

CONSTRUCTIVE
WORDS

words that give honor

words that bring hope

guidance

words that promote faith

consolation

instruction

edification (words that build up)

inspiration

rebukes (see Prov. 9:8)

encouraging words

CONCLUSION

Whoever has your heart has your life. Proverbs 4:23 tells us that out of the heart springs all of life—your marriage, your family, your friends, everyone you have a relationship with. None of us hopes that these relationships will fail; we want to grow old with our spouses, remain close to our children and grandchildren, and savor friendships that have lasted for decades. At some point you won your spouse's heart, your friend's heart; or they won yours. The only way those relationships will continue to flourish is if we keep the hearts we have won. That's where many of us find ourselves at a loss—but as we've learned over the last seven weeks, the ways we keep someone's heart are the same ways we first won it.

We've discovered seven powerful keys that unlock the human heart. Love—given freely, without conditions. Faith—believing more for someone than they believe for themselves. Interest—people are interested in those who are interested in them. Availability—people want to be with someone who makes them a priority. Respect—demonstrating a person's value. Time—one of the most powerful keys to unlocking a heart. Last of all, Communication—the lifeline of any relationship.

Before we hit the road, a word of caution—these seven keys are not magic spells. Relationships are not a one-way street, though we often behave as if they were. The common thread in all seven keys is that your focus is on the other person—not on yourself. If we choose to focus on ourselves instead, we are in danger of misusing the truths we've discussed here to manipulate someone else into cooperating with our agenda. Manipulation can take many forms, but all of them center on the question of *what's best for me*. Rather than investing our energy in benefiting the other person and thinking of any benefit we receive as a bonus, we are tempted to override them and find shortcuts to what we want.

But a relationship that will last for the long haul cannot be built overnight, or without the cooperation of the other person. We must make ourselves students of our loved ones, and make the cultivation of our relationships a daily priority. If we neglect to regularly care for the needs of our spouse, or child, or friend, the day will come when those relationships die, whether at the end of a long, slow slide or under the weight of a blow they no longer have the strength to withstand. Yet there is a powerful truth on the flip side of this coin—if we do the hard, disciplined work of watering, feeding, and fertilizing the relationships we have, those relationships will become strong, able to withstand and even benefit from the storms of life. A healthy relationship is hard to lose.

Perhaps you've realized that it's been a long time since you put in that hard, relationship-building work. It isn't too late to begin building a new legacy. Start right now. As we give unconditional love, express faith, put others first, are there when they need us, give them respect, invest our time in them, and keep the lifeline of communication open, we will slowly but surely win the hearts of those we love.

seven

THREE SIMPLE GOALS

MEET

Prioritize building relationships. Life-change happens best in the context of relationships.

MENTOR

Life is a journey, and everyone is at a different place on that journey. Help people take just one step further in their faith.

MULTIPLY

Multiply disciples by inviting people to your group and/or by conducting an outreach as a group. Multiply leaders by sharing ownership.

HOST INFO

Thank you for responding to the opportunity to host a Small Group. Whether you are hosting for the first time or for the hundredth time, we believe that you will be blessed as you serve.

BE YOURSELF. God wants you to use your unique gifts and temperament, so lead in a way that fits you and in a way that is best for the group. When you don't have an answer, admit it; when you make a mistake, apologize. Honesty and friendliness go a long way.

SHOULDER-TAP TO GROW. A shoulder-tap is when you personally invite someone into your group. Begin by shoulder-tapping your family, neighbors, coworkers, friends from church, etc. If you and your group members do this, then your group will have everyone who is supposed to be there.

SHARE OWNERSHIP. Don't try to do it alone. You may be perfectly capable of opening up your home, bringing the food, and leading the discussion each time you meet, but when you allow others to help, you give them an opportunity to grow in their faith and gifts.

PREPARE AHEAD OF TIME. Before each meeting, preview the session and write down your responses to each question.

PRAY FOR YOUR GROUP MEMBERS. Heart transformation only happens when God is involved. Commit to pray for your Small Group meetings and for each group member.

BREAK UP INTO SMALLER GROUPS IF YOUR GROUP GETS TOO BIG. If your group has more than ten people, we strongly encourage you to have the group gather in discussion circles of five or six people. A small circle encourages quieter members to participate and gives everyone a greater opportunity to be heard.

Host FAQs

Who is in charge?

Most groups have an official Host—a person who coordinates and facilitates the group meetings. The Host may lead the group's discussions personally, or may take turns with other group members. Ideally, as the group matures, members will share the leadership of the group. We have discovered that healthy groups rotate Hosts and homes on a regular basis. Shared ownership in the group ensures that all members grow, give their unique contribution, and develop their gifts.

How many people should my group have?

Minimum is you +2. Think of gathering a few friends, not necessarily having a full house. You might choose to meet with another couple who would enjoy walking through this study.

Should our group meet before the series begins?

Yes! A get-to-know-you party is a fantastic way to begin building relationships.

How do I structure each meeting?

The goal of Small Groups is not only to discuss, but to build relationships. Your group should seek to follow the session order for each week as laid out in this study guide. We also recommend incorporating a meal or refreshments, a time to just hang out, and periodic gatherings outside of the scheduled group meetings.

How much time per week will this study take?

The group meeting time can be anywhere from 1½ hours to as long as you'd like.

How long will this group meet?

As the Host, please commit to meet for the duration of the seven-week study. At the end of that time, you can decide whether you and your group want to continue meeting. If your group wants to continue but you'd like a break from hosting, we encourage another member of the group to take a turn in this role. If you find that the group doesn't seem to be connecting for you, don't give up. This can be a result of personality conflicts, life stage differences, geographical distance, levels of spiritual maturity, or any number of things. God often uses uncomfortable situations to teach us, so we encourage you to stick with it for the seven weeks! At the end of the study, decide whether to continue with this group or find another.

Do I have to pray aloud?

If you're not comfortable praying aloud, just ask if someone else would like to start and end the group in prayer. However, we encourage you to step out of your comfort zone.

Do I need a lot of Bible knowledge to host?

No, you do not. You will enjoy learning along with everyone else in the group.

How do we handle the childcare needs in our group?

There are a number of ways to approach this issue. You may try one option that works for a while and then adjust over time. Some possibilities:

- Have the adults meet in the living room or dining room and share the cost of a babysitter (or two) who can watch the kids in a different part of the house. This way, parents don't have to be away from their children all evening if their children are too young to be left at home.
- Use one home for the kids and a second home (close by or a phone call away) for the adults.
- Rotate the responsibility of providing a lesson or care for the children, either in the same home or in another home nearby. This can be an incredible blessing for kids.
- Let group members make their own arrangements for childcare.

No matter what decision the group makes, the best approach is to dialogue openly about both the problem and the solution.

ALSO BY
MICHAEL
FLETCHER

LifeGiving Marriage

A six-week study by Michael and Laura Fletcher

The design for marriage was formulated by God in the Garden of Eden...before sin came into the human race. God intended it to be an awe-inspiring, intimate, fruitful, joyous relationship—in short, life-giving! Marriage should be a source of joy to both husband and wife, and a source of strength, confidence, and encouragement to all the members of the family. This six-week study is designed to help us rediscover God's design for the LifeGiving Marriage.

The Kingdom

A six-week study by Michael Fletcher with Jeff Christensen

An angel imposter: cloaked in darkness and armed with pride and greed. A coup: devastation prevails on the planet, and poisons the soul of man. A divine revolutionary: filled with power and light, armed with truth, clothed in humility. It's a story of violence and peace—of intrigue and romance—of revolution and redemption. It's a story as ancient as time itself...and this all-encompassing epic includes us all.

These studies and more available at www.RightNowMedia.org or at the Manna Church World Café bookstore. Visit https://www.rightnow.org/Account/Invite/Manna to gain access to Right Now Media.

Building Successful Relationships

Our quality of life is largely measured by the success or failure of our relationships. We all hunger for lasting, life-giving relationships with our spouses, parents, children, coworkers, friends, and others around us—but these relationships can be a struggle to establish or even maintain. Whether you want to increase intimacy in your current relationships, develop new ones, or repair those that have been damaged, the seven practical keys in *Building Successful Relationships* can draw your heart and the hearts of those around you closer together.

Overcoming Barriers to Church Growth

Passionate about church growth, Michael Fletcher understands the obstacles pastors and church leaders face as they reach 100-200 and 700-800 member barriers. He lays out clear, practical steps churches can follow to achieve the growth they desire. His strategies have proved effective not only in his church, which has grown dramatically, but also across the nation.

E-book also available on Kindle and Amazon

How To Get Promoted

If you want to get promoted, ask advice from the person who makes the decision! Michael sought the expert advice of 31 successful business leaders, entrepreneurs, pastors, and military leaders—people who make and break careers. Their surprising insights, combined with the clear teaching of Scripture, make this book a must-read for anyone wanting to get ahead in life. Soundly biblical, unashamedly practical, and sometimes in-your-face, *How to Get Promoted* will prepare you to go to the next level!

Beyond Reconciliation
with Larry Jackson

We hear many Christian leaders preaching the need for racial reconciliation in our country—but we don't see much real change taking place in our churches. Why do so few people experience true friendships with brothers or sisters of a different cultural background? Why are so few churches multi-ethnic? The fact is that the message of reconciliation is only the starting point. In sharing their own story of an extraordinary covenant friendship across cultural boundaries, Larry and Michael shed light on the perspectives, leadership, and initiative that can produce hope and lasting reconciliation.

Available for purchase at the Manna Church World Café bookstore